How Fi

to the world:

A Play

by Gary Bedel
illustrated by Len Ebert

Printed in the United States of America

ISBN 0-15-317296-7 – How Fire Came to the World: A Play

Ordering Options
ISBN 0-15-318644-5 (Package of 5)
ISBN 0-15-316987-7 (Grade 3 Package)

1 2 3 4 5 6 7 8 9 10 179 02 01 00 99

Cast

Ish (mother)
Nop (father)
Bo (their son)
Fir (their daughter)
Om (Bo's pet wolf)

SCENE 1

(The cave of the Urg family and the land around it. Inside the cave are a few rock chairs. There are some beds on the floor.)

ISH *(wrapping her arms around herself)*: It's so cold in here!

NOP *(to ISH)*: You know it will be cold until spring. It always is.

1

FIR: I want some warm food!

NOP: Now, dear, you know there won't be any warm food until spring, either.

FIR *(scowling)*: I hate the cold! I want to go to a warm place!

ISH: Now, none of that. It will be spring soon.

BO: I wish I could make it warm. *(petting OM)* You would like it to be warm, too, wouldn't you? *(OM nods his head.)*

ISH: Enough of that. Let's sit down and have a peaceful brunch.

2

BO *(to himself and still patting OM)*: There must be something we can do. I have an idea! *(He runs outside the cave with OM.)*

FIR *(to herself)*: He is so silly. *(BO and OM return with rocks.)*

BO: Here!

FIR: Here what?

BO: We can use these to keep warm! The last time the volcano was erupting, the lava made these rocks! Maybe they will still be warm. We can put them on us when we sleep! *(He lies down and puts the rocks on top of him. They roll off.)*

FIR *(walking offstage)*: I hate rocks, too!

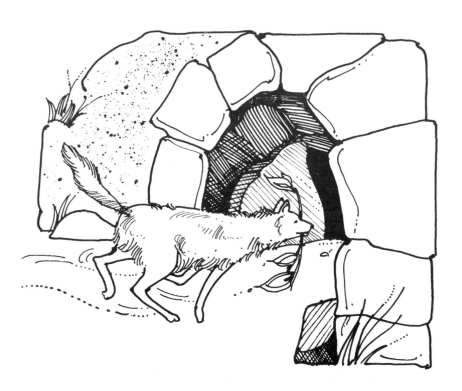

(Suddenly, OM runs offstage.)

BO: Where are you going? Come back, Om! Come back! *(to FIR)* See what you did? Now my wolf is gone!

(OM returns with a stick in his mouth. It is on fire.)

BO *(looking at the stick)*: Wow! What is that?

FIR *(screaming)*: Mom! Dad! The wolf is trying to hurt us! Come quickly!

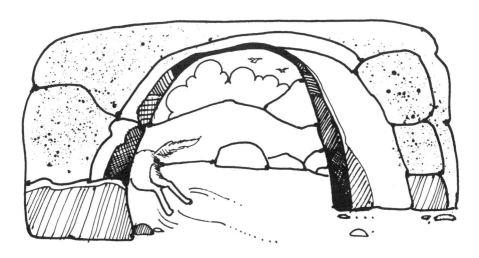

(ISH and NOP come rushing in.)

ISH: What is that wolf doing? Get him out of here! *(She runs after OM, who escapes out of the cave.)*

NOP *(to BO)*: I told you that wolf would be trouble! I don't want to see it back in here ever again!

BO: Please, Dad! Om would never try to hurt us!

NOP: Son, it's just too dangerous. *(sneezes)* Besides, I'm allergic to him.

BO: I have to find him! *(He runs out to find OM.)*

ISH: Don't bring back that dangerous wolf!

SCENE 2

(Outside the cave. BO and OM are sitting together a short distance from the cave.)

BO *(petting OM)*: I know you would never hurt us, but my dad was really angry.

(OM puts his head on BO's lap. Then he gets up and looks offstage. He barks.)

BO: What are you saying, boy? What do you want me to see?

(OM barks again. He puts his paw on BO and looks offstage.)

6

BO: What are you telling me? Over there is the lava that keeps erupting from that volcano. *(OM nods strongly.)*

BO: Well, what about it? It's red. It's hot. Is that it? It's hot? Om, it's very far away. I tried to use lava rocks to stay warm, but they aren't hot now. *(OM trots away and comes back with the burning stick. He puts it at BO's feet. BO holds his hand near it.)*

BO: Hot. It's hot. Is there something we could do with this to keep warm? *(OM nods excitedly.)*

BO: Let's see. (*He looks at the burning stick.*) We could eat it.

(*OM shakes his head. Then he gets up and brings more sticks to the fire. In a while, the fire is very big.*)

BO: I'm getting hot, Om. (*His eyes open wide.*) I'm getting hot! That's it, isn't it! I'm getting hot! We could keep ourselves warm! Great, Om! (*He hugs OM. Then OM breaks away. He brings back an egg in his mouth.*)

8

BO: Now what? *(He watches as OM drops the egg on a hot rock near the fire. The egg cooks.)* I see what you're doing! Warm food! *(He tastes the cooked egg.)* This is delicious! Om, you are the smartest wolf in the world.

(OM beams and wags his tail.)

BO *(with his head propped on his hands)*: The tricky part will be getting everyone else to understand.

SCENE 3

(Back inside the cave ISH, NOP, and FIR are sitting shivering.)

BO *(at the opening of the cave):* Mom? Dad? Can I show you something?

ISH: Does it have to do with that wolf?

BO: Well, yes—

ISH: Then no! We are trying to have a peaceful day!

BO: But Mom!

NOP: You heard your mother!

BO *(Outside the cave, BO stands thinking. Then he snaps his fingers.)*: I know! He begins to gather sticks. Om! Here, boy! Go get the fire!
(OM trots away and comes back with the burning branch.)
BO: Put it there on those twigs. *(The twigs catch fire.)* Now, Om, go get some eggs! *(Om races away and comes back with them.)*
BO: Good boy! *(BO cooks the eggs on a rock near the fire. He folds them over gently.)*

ISH: What's that smell? *(The family comes out of the cave.)*

FIR: That smells wonderful! What is it?

BO: I call this dish an omelet, after Om. We will have warm food, Fir! We can be warm, Mom! Om showed me how to do it. We will never have to be cold again!

NOP *(getting close to the fire and rubbing his hands together)*: By golly, that's warm. *(He takes a handful of the eggs and eats them.)* Your omelet would make a fine brunch dish. This wolf taught you that?

BO: Yes, sir. All of it.

NOP *(looking at OM):* I guess I owe you an apology, Om. I may be allergic, but you can stay. You have changed our lives. We will share your gift with everyone we meet. Tales of your cleverness will be told for years and years to come.

How Was It Discovered?

Think of something you use every day. What would your life be like without this item? Write a story about how this item was discovered. Draw pictures to go with your story.

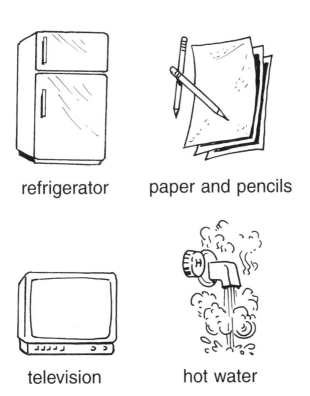

refrigerator   paper and pencils

television   hot water

School-Home Connection Invite your child to read the play aloud with you. You may want to take different parts and make props for eggs, rocks, and burning sticks.

TAKE-HOME BOOK
Hidden Surprises
Use with "Little Grunt and the Big Egg."